CW00536991

The Ultimate Guide to Manage and Stress Relief how to Identify Your Stress Warning Signs and Learn how to Better Manage Stressful Situations

Brian Gibson

Published by vincenzo nappi, 2022.

THE ULTIMATE GUIDE TO MANAGE AND STRESS RELIEF HOW TO IDENTIFY YOUR STRESS WARNING SIGNS AND LEARN HOW TO BETTER MANAGE STRESSFUL SITUATIONS

First edition. December 25, 2022.

Copyright © 2022 Brian Gibson.

ISBN: 979-8215565988

Written by Brian Gibson.

Also by Brian Gibson

Table of Contents

The Ultimate Guide to Manage and Stress Relief

How to Identify Your Stress Warning Signs and Learn how to Better Manage Stressful Situations

Brian Gibson

Chapter One

How the Stress Response Works

———

Traffic jams, a deadline approaching quickly, a concerning illness, or a contentious argument with your spouse could all be examples of stress. A friend might describe it as a failing relationship, the need to care for a sick parent or a mountain of unpaid bills. However, if you were a medical professional, you would classify these events as stressors or stressful situations. A broader definition of stress is a physical reaction that occurs automatically in response to any stimulus that necessitates adaptation to change. Every actual or imagined threat to your body, such as a sudden car crash, a loud argument, or the pain of rheumatoid arthritis, sets off a chain reaction of stress hormones that results in well-coordinated physiological changes. We all have firsthand experience with these feelings. Your heart is racing. Tensed muscles. Sweat beads appear as breathing becomes more rapid. But for a long time, researchers have been curious about the precise mechanisms underlying these reactions, their causes, and potential long-term effects.

Walter B. Cannon, a Harvard physiologist, was a pioneer in studying the biochemistry of stress. His research conducted nearly a century ago persuaded him that the adrenal glands, located on top of the kidneys, also contribute to fear. Cannon successfully isolated a hormone secreted by the adrenal glands of scared cats during tests with caged cats and barking dogs. He administered that hormone to a second, completely calm cat, and it caused a startling physical fear response. The cat's heart rate, blood pressure, and blood flow to its muscles suddenly increased. This occurrence was Cannon's "fright, fight, or flight" response. However, it is now referred to as the "fight-or-flight response" or the "stress response." Epinephrine was the first hormone Cannon was able to isolate. Adrenaline is another name derived from the glands that produce it. Next, Cannon discovered norepinephrine, also known as noradrenaline, a second stress-response hormone. Cortisol, a member of the second class of stress hormones known as glucocorticoids and a key player in the stress response, was discovered by other researchers.

A signal from the hypothalamus, a brain region, triggers the stress response. The autonomic nervous system connects the network of nerves in the hypothalamus, perched above the brain stem, to the rest of your body. The autonomic nervous system controls automatic bodily processes like breathing, blood pressure, heartbeat, and the expansion or contraction of bronchioles, which are tiny airways in the lungs. It has two tributaries: the parasympathetic nervous system, which calms the body after the threat has passed, and the sympathetic nervous system, which stimulates the body in response to perceived threats. The corticotropin-releasing factor (CRF), a chemical messenger, is sent from the hypothalamus to the nearby pituitary gland when the hypothalamus processes certain information, such as the sight of your boss approaching you with a menacing expression or the sound of screeching tires behind you. Adrenocorticotropic hormone (ACTH), the chemical messenger produced by the pituitary gland in response to this stimulation, is sent to the adrenal glands, releasing cortisol into the bloodstream. On orders from the brain, the adrenal glands also release bursts of noradrenaline and adrenaline, which are simultaneously distributed throughout the body by the sympathetic nervous system. (The HPA axis is the name given to the potent trio of the hypothalamus, pituitary, and adrenal glands. It controls many hormonal processes in the body and acts as a feedback mechanism to help turn off the stress response when certain hormone levels become excessive).

As you prepare to fight or flee, stress hormones rush through your bloodstream to various parts of your body. As your body absorbs more oxygen, your breathing becomes more rapid. Glucose and fats that give you energy are released from storage locations into your bloodstream. You become more alert when your senses, such as sight and hearing, are sharper. Your blood pressure increases, and your heart beats up to two to three times as quickly as usual. Blood flow is helped to be directed toward your muscles and brain and away from your skin and other organs by certain blood vessels constricting. As platelets, which are blood cells, become stickier, clots can form more quickly, reducing bleeding from potential wounds. The immune system becomes more active. Your muscles, even the tiny, hair-raising ones under your skin, tense up as you prepare to take action. The suppression of bodily functions is not required for the current emergency. The intestines and stomach stop working. Reduced sexual arousal. Body tissue growth and repair slow down. Cannon thought that the stress reaction was transient. He reasoned that the body would wind down to its average balance, also known as homeostasis, minutes after the adrenaline-induced rush. Your lungs would therefore breathe more slowly as a result. As your heart rate slowed and your blood started to flow normally once more, your blood pressure would decrease. Your intestines would begin to function again, supplying fresh fuel to replenish the energy expended during the emergency. Bones would start to heal or grow once more, and sex might seem more alluring. The daily operations of your body would resume once the challenge that triggered the stress response was over and the parasympathetic nervous system was working its calming magic. But later studies revealed that Cannon was not entirely right.

The stress response can be incredibly beneficial, as many people have pointed out. People can accomplish Herculean feats thanks to a surge in adrenaline. Who can forget the firefighters who, following the terrorist attacks of September 11, 2001, charged up several flights of smoke-filled stairs in the World Trade Center while carrying lifesaving equipment? Or the ordinary people who helped the injured and disabled leave the towers? In such overwhelming circumstances, fight-or-flight reactions are appropriate and crucial. The stress response, when used properly, aids in our ability to overcome many obstacles. These obstacles could be natural disasters like a fire or an earthquake or internal dangers like a circulatory system that is in danger of collapsing fatally.

The fight-or-flight response can be helpful in much less dangerous situations as well. The idea that physical and psychosocial stressors elicit the same physiological response was advanced by physiologist Hans Selye, whose work contributed to the development of modern stress theory. Selye studied the difference between short-term stress (also known as "good" stress), which motivates people to mobilize their resources to overcome challenges, and ongoing or excessive stress (also known as "bad" stress or distress). Robert M. Yerkes and John D. Dodson, two Harvard researchers, also showed that a sudden spike in stress isn't always bad. They observed that, up to a point, performance and efficiency increased as stress or anxiety levels did.

Further stress and anxiety caused a significant decline in capability and performance at this crucial point. The location of that turning point seems to vary from person to person. Because even though humans and other animals have a hard-wired stress response, the situations and viewpoints that trigger it differ significantly. Your neighbor might easily ignore or even enjoy what you see as dangerous. Scientists have investigated why some people seem less susceptible to stress or even thrive on regular doses. According to some research, people who can handle stress have certain traits in common. Social support and exercise turned out to be crucial. Control, difficulty, and commitment all improved. Stress-resistant individuals seem to have a sense of control or the ability to influence events, take on challenges in circumstances that other people might find stressful, and identify with a meaningful cause. One study found that individuals with these traits report fewer illnesses and are less likely to miss work.

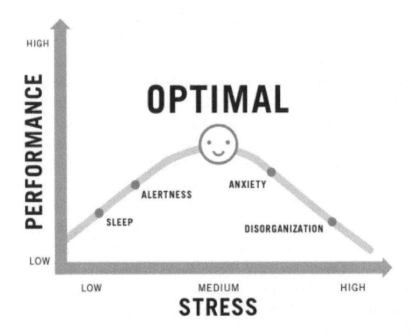

Yerkes-Dodson law

The stress response makes sense intuitively. It enables us to respond to situations and events that value our enhanced abilities and awareness. When you see a bus barreling toward you, the adrenaline rush helps you sprint away much more quickly than you would normally. The ideal physical outlet was found for the stress hormones that entered your bloodstream at the sight of the bus. But based on experience, we know that not only situations involving obvious dangers cause us to react in that way. Any circumstance that makes you feel threatened or necessitates a change in your behavior could do the same. That's where things get complicated. Your body is not very good at distinguishing between potentially fatal situations and regularly stressful circumstances. Anger or worry brought on by less significant stressors like financial worries or not finding a quick physical release is stuck in traffic and tends to increase throughout the day. Increasing the turmoil is the expectation of upcoming issues, such as what you might go through while awaiting the outcomes of a medical examination. The physical and psychological signs of stress, including clenched teeth, trembling, and anxious feelings, add to this, resulting in a destructive, self-reinforcing cycle. Worrisome health issues can develop when your body repeatedly experiences the stress response or when arousal following a terrible trauma is never completely switched off. High blood pressure, also known as hypertension, a significant risk factor for heart disease, is a good illustration of this. Another is immune system suppression, which makes people more vulnerable to common illnesses like colds. It's impossible to avoid every stressor, nor would you want to. Physical and psychological challenges are a constant in our lives; they give life a zest and occasionally bring about satisfying results. While it may be difficult to completely eliminate some sources of stress, you can learn to view them differently and adjust how you react to them.

Psychological scars from traumatic events are expected. Post-traumatic stress disorder symptoms were common among those who fled or witnessed the destruction of the World Trade Center during the September 11 attacks and the rescue workers who flocked to the area (PTSD). Military personnel who have participated in combat, most recently in Afghanistan and Iraq, have done the same. The National Center for Posttraumatic Stress Disorder estimates that up to 30% of Vietnam veterans, 6% to 11% of Afghan war veterans, and 12% to 20% of Iraq war veterans have PTSD. PTSD may also be brought on by other traumatic incidents, including rape, physical assault, accidents, natural disasters, living in a violent area such as a war zone, and unexpectedly losing a loved one. People with a family history of depression are more likely to develop PTSD.

Its primary signs are as follows:

✓ persistent nightmares, intrusive thoughts, or flashbacks to a traumatic event;

✓ avoiding people and specific situations;

✓ avoiding reminders of the incident or having trouble remembering it;

✓ trouble sleeping;

✓ being overly alert or susceptible to startles.

Not every survivor of a traumatic event goes on to develop PTSD. Even if your immediate reaction to a disaster is extreme, this does not indicate that you have a mental or emotional disorder. Try reaching out to others and returning to your routine to find comfort. Exercise, relaxation techniques, and focusing on the future while expressing emotions may also be beneficial. However, if symptoms persist for over a few weeks, you should get assistance from a qualified mental health professional. Also, remember that symptoms may not appear for six months or longer after the triggering event.

Stress can also fuel or contribute to depression and anxiety. Adopting the recommendations in this report could aid in preventing these issues. Using stress-management techniques can help with anxiety and depression symptoms, but it's important to consult a qualified healthcare provider first. They can assess you and suggest a medication-counseling combination, a mind-body program, or other stress-management techniques. Get a professional opinion if your anxiety is too intense to interfere with your daily life. Any of the following signs could be present:

✓ Consistently feeling extremely anxious or afraid or repeatedly feeling panicky;

✓ irrational fear, dread, or danger feelings;

✓ persistent physical symptoms without a valid threat, such as restlessness, trembling, nausea, hot flashes, dizziness, shortness of breath, or the need to urinate frequently;

✓ repeated, upsetting thoughts and uncontrollable, repetitive behaviors meant to ease the anxiety they cause.

Likewise, if you experience any of the following depressive symptoms, it's crucial to consult a medical professional:

✓ Protracted melancholy or irritability.

✓ Loss of interest in once-enjoyable activities.

✓ Significantly more or less than usual sleeping or eating.

✓ Guilt, worthlessness, or hopelessness feelings.

✓ Being agitated and unable to remain still.

✓ Difficulty focusing and making choices.

Depression symptoms such as recurrent thoughts of suicide or death necessitate prompt medical intervention.

Chapter two

Stressful Life

———

C hances are good that you'll endure some extremely stressful experiences throughout your lifetime. Additionally, you'll experience a variety of much lesser daily stressors. You can identify the stress warning signs in your life with the list provided later in this section. When you know how stress affects your feelings and behaviors, you can use the numerous tools discussed here to lessen its effects. A scale that measured the stress of significant life events was developed by two psychiatrists at the University of Washington in the 1980s, asking 394 men and women to rank various scenarios. The subjects were asked to rate a list of other life events while keeping in mind that marriage equaled 50 out of a possible 100 units. After that, their responses were averaged.

The Holmes-Rahe Life Stress Inventory
The Social Readjustment Rating Scale

INSTRUCTIONS: Mark down the point value of each of these life events that has happened to you during the previous year. Total these associated points.

Life Event	Mean Value
1. Death of spouse	100
2. Divorce	73
3. Marital Separation from mate	65
4. Detention in jail or other institution	63
5. Death of a close family member	63
6. Major personal injury or illness	53
7. Marriage	50
8. Being fired at work	47
9. Marital reconciliation with mate	45
10. Retirement from work	45
11. Major change in the health or behavior of a family member	44
12. Pregnancy	40
13. Sexual Difficulties	39
14. Gaining a new family member (i.e.. birth, adoption, older adult moving in, etc)	39
15. Major business readjustment	39
16. Major change in financial state (i.e.. a lot worse or better off than usual)	38
17. Death of a close friend	37
18. Changing to a different line of work	36
19. Major change in the number of arguments w/spouse (i.e.. either a lot more or a lot less than usual regarding child rearing, personal habits, etc.)	35
20. Taking on a mortgage (for home, business, etc..)	31
21. Foreclosure on a mortgage or loan	30
22. Major change in responsibilities at work (i.e. promotion, demotion, etc.)	29
23. Son or daughter leaving home (marriage, attending college, joined mil.)	29
24. In-law troubles	29
25. Outstanding personal achievement	28
26. Spouse beginning or ceasing work outside the home	26
27. Beginning or ceasing formal schooling	26
28. Major change in living condition (new home, remodeling, deterioration of neighborhood or home etc.)	25
29. Revision of personal habits (dress manners, associations, quitting smoking)	24
30. Troubles with the boss	23
31. Major changes in working hours or conditions	20
32. Changes in residence	20
33. Changing to a new school	20
34. Major change in usual type and/or amount of recreation	19
35. Major change in church activity (i.e.. a lot more or less than usual)	19
36. Major change in social activities (clubs, movies,visiting, etc.)	18
37. Taking on a loan (car, tv,freezer,etc)	17
38. Major change in sleeping habits (a lot more or a lot less than usual)	16
39. Major change in number of family get-togethers ("")	15
40. Major change in eating habits (a lot more or less food intake, or very different meal hours or surroundings)	15
41. Vacation	13
42. Major holidays	12
43. Minor violations of the law (traffic tickets, jaywalking, disturbing the peace, etc)	11

Now, add up all the points you have to find your score.

150pts or less means a relatively low amount of life change and a low susceptibility to stress-induced health breakdown.

150 to 300 pts implies about a 50% chance of a major health breakdown in the next 2 years.

300pts or more raises the odds to about 80%, according to the Holmes-Rahe statistical prediction model.

The creators of the scale, Thomas Holmes and Richard Rahe observed in later studies that the death of a spouse, which ranks highest on the scale, appeared to have a significant effect on health.

Compared to other people in their age group, spouses who survived were 10 times more likely to pass away in the following year. Couples who divorced also had a 12 times higher risk of falling ill the next year than those who remained married. Researchers have widely used the scale to examine how stress affects people. It has limitations, though. The age of the study may limit its applicability today.

Additionally, it only covers significant events, which only make up a small portion of daily stressors. Simple daily stressors like standing in line for hours, sitting in traffic, or dealing with work demands can add up and jeopardize your physical and mental health. A scale is primarily a research tool but can also be useful for people outside the field. It might be helpful to know that others have described an event you may be going through, like a job change, as being particularly stressful. The fact that many of the events on the scale aren't immediately harmful is intriguing. Celebrating a marriage, a new baby or a remarkable personal accomplishment may seem appropriate. But many changes can be positive, negative, or even a little bit of both. Actually, how stress is perceived depends on the individual. The scale can act as a reminder as well. Spend more time practicing stress management and other self-help techniques if you're managing one or more of the stressors listed on the significant life event stress scale. Most likely, you are aware of how you respond under pressure. Important events undoubtedly draw attention, as do apparent signs of distress. However, smaller waves might fly under your radar. Making a note of exactly how stress affects you will help you recognize your own personal stress warning signs earlier so you can stop unneeded stress reactions.

You probably have your own strategies for coping with pressure. Some might be beneficial, like making a friend-related call, preparing a hearty meal, or retiring earlier than usual. Some people might not be as kind. All too frequently, people seek relief from pressure by self-medicating or engaging in other unhealthy habits. They could accomplish this in numerous ways. For instance:

✓ watching a lot of television;

✓ avoiding problems by withdrawing from friends or partners or, alternatively, hopping into a frenetic social life;

✓ binge eating or gaining weight;

✓ under eating or losing weight;

✓ excessive slumber;

✓ abusing alcohol to excess;

✓ exhibiting emotional or physically violent outbursts when lashing out at others;

✓ starting to smoke or smoking more frequently than usual;

✓ using over-the-counter or prescription medications that promise to provide relief, such as sedatives, muscle relaxants, or anti-anxiety medications;

✓ using dangerous or illegal drugs.

Making healthy decisions can be aided by becoming aware of your typical stress management techniques. Instead of reaching for a sugary snack, for instance, you might choose to call a friend. Instead of consuming, choosing to connect can help you de-stress. Studies show that emphasizing social ties can bring health advantages without adding calories.

Chapter three

Managing and preventing stress

A cardiologist by the name of Herbert Benson conducted groundbreaking research into the harmful effects of stress and the body's capacity for self-healing in the late 1970s while working in the same Harvard Medical School lab where Cannon had toiled years earlier. Since then, he and numerous other researchers have studied stress response, relaxation response, and various stress-reducing methods. The report's medical editor, Dr. Benson, is also the head of the Massachusetts General Hospital's Benson-Henry Institute for Mind-Body Medicine, which promotes various stress-reduction techniques. They include:

✓ acquiring a variety of relaxation-inducing skills, such as breath control and body scanning;

✓ Taking care of yourself by scheduling time for leisure, socializing, exercising, making friends, and engaging in activities that make you happy;

✓ utilizing cognitive restructuring, a technique that enables you to reframe negative beliefs so you can deal with a situation more skillfully.

Such self-care is a crucial component of being healthy. Cardiovascular illness serves as an illustration of how it can have an impact. Millions of Americans currently take medicine to reduce their risk of heart disease risk factors like high blood pressure and unhealthy cholesterol levels. Angioplasty and coronary artery bypass surgery are surgical techniques that can unblock clogged blood arteries or redirect blood flow to healthier vessels. Medication and medical treatments are two beneficial options. However, when used separately, they only make up two of a robust three-legged stool that exemplifies the best in contemporary healthcare. Effective self-care techniques make up the third leg. According to research, routinely inducing the relaxation response lowers blood pressure levels permanently. Blood pressure can be reduced through stress-management methods like cognitive restructuring that block the stress reaction. A healthy diet and frequent exercise can raise blood pressure and cholesterol levels. Additionally, social support has a potent health-protective effect. Combining these self-care techniques may prevent serious outcomes and lessen or even eliminate the need for some medications over time.

The relaxation response, the antithesis of the stress reaction, can be induced willfully to induce a deep sense of calm and rest. A physiological alteration called the relaxation response slows down the metabolic changes that initially sent us into overdrive. You can aid your body in lessening the cumulative effects of stress by routinely practicing relaxation techniques. Several physiological alterations take place during the relaxation response. For instance, heart and respiration rates slow when people use relaxation response strategies. The body uses less oxygen, and blood moves more freely throughout it. Blood lactate levels drop significantly, which some researchers think may be related to anxiety attacks. There are numerous strategies to trigger the relaxation response, including these:

✓ breath focus

✓ mindfulness

✓ guided imagery or vision

✓ body scan

✓ Qi gong, yoga, or tai chi

✓ continual prayer

There are other methods as well that can cause the relaxation response. You could discover that some are really good. The technique must allow you to focus on a word, phrase, prayer, or repeating muscle movement to break up your regular thoughts. Once mastered, these skills can be consistently exercised in practically any place. There is no need for specialized gear or a professional trainer, but many people find that attending yoga or meditation classes can be helpful as they acquire a new skill. You can gain by trying techniques to induce calm rather than sticking with just one. You can use it to decide which approaches are best for you.

Additionally, you will have a backup plan if your favorite occasionally fails to hold your attention. In fact, many people find that combining numerous strategies yields the best results. When creating your regimen, you might find it helpful to keep in mind the following advice:

• Look for a serene location to sit or lie down.

• Focus. Pick a specific focus, such as your breath, a sound, a word, or a phrase you repeat out loud or in your head.

• Recognize how to unwind and "let go." Accept whatever thoughts, emotions, or sensations come up.

• • Regular practice—aim for once or twice every day. Maintaining a regular schedule can strengthen the ritualistic feeling, which will make practicing easier for you. Since making time later in the day can be challenging, many people elicit the relaxation response in the morning before breakfast. Evidence supports the idea that the more frequently you use these strategies, the better the results.

• • Aim for between 10 and 20 minutes per day.

A straightforward yet effective strategy for inducing relaxation in people from all backgrounds is breath focus. However, occasionally, health issues could make utilizing this method problematic. Learning how to breathe correctly is the first step in developing breath focus. Learning good breathing techniques is the first step in using breath focus, a stress-reduction strategy. Your diaphragm contracts as you inhale, giving your lungs the space they require to expand. Your chest and belly should rise and feel your lungs fill entirely if you breathe correctly. Your diaphragm presses up against your lungs as you exhale, aiding in releasing carbon dioxide. Your belly will drop when you exhale if you're breathing deeply. There are various terms for good breathing. It has also been referred to as belly, abdominal, and diaphragmatic. Your lower belly will rise as you inhale deeply, allowing the air entering your nose to completely fill your lungs. There are plenty of people who can breathe so forcefully and profoundly. This talent is innate but frequently goes untapped. You can access one of your body's most powerful self-healing processes by reawakening it. Why do so many of us find deep breathing to be unnatural? One explanation could be that our society frequently rewards us for suppressing powerful emotions. Women and girls are supposed to control their rage. Men and boys are advised not to cry. What occurs when you stop your feelings, such as your tears, wrath, fear, or pain, during a heated argument? You unknowingly hold your breath or breathe erratically. Breathing is also influenced by one's body image.

Men and women are encouraged to contract their stomach muscles since our culture considers a "washboard" stomach so desirable. As a result, stress and worry increase, and shallow "chest breathing" gradually starts to feel normal. The diaphragm, a robust strip of muscle that separates the chest from the abdomen, is activated during breathing. The diaphragm descends when you breathe in, drawing your lungs down with it and pressing against your abdominal organs to create space for your lungs to expand as they fill with air. The diaphragm pushes back against your lungs as you exhale, aiding in releasing carbon dioxide. The range of motion of the diaphragm is restricted by shallow breathing. The lower part of the lungs, which contains numerous tiny blood veins essential for delivering oxygen to cells, never receives its fair share of oxygenated air. You may have breathlessness and anxiety as a result. Full oxygen exchange, or the advantageous exchange of incoming oxygen for exiting carbon dioxide, is promoted by deep abdominal breathing. This breathing naturally slows the heartbeat and can reduce or maintain blood pressure.

The foundation of breath concentration is diaphragmatic breathing, which is easy to do:

First steps. Locate a peaceful, cozy spot to sit or lie down. Begin by focusing on your breath. Take a regular breath first. Try inhaling slowly and deeply now. Your lower belly should fill with the air that enters through your nose. Allow your belly to fully expand. Now exhale from your nose (or mouth, if that seems more comfortable). Take numerous deep breaths in between regular ones. Pay close attention to how you feel when you breathe in and out regularly and deeply. While deep breathing results in relaxation, shallow breathing frequently feels tight and restricted. Now spend a few minutes practicing diaphragmatic breathing. Place one hand on the area of your belly right below the belly button. Every time you inhale, feel your hand rise about an inch, and every time you exhale, feel it descend about an inch. Together with your abdomen, your chest will also increase a little. Remember to relax your tummy so it can expand entirely with each breath.

Breath focus. After completing the steps above, you can regularly practice breath focus. Blend your breathing with a concentration word or phrase that will help you relax while you sit comfortably with your eyes closed. Imagine that every breath you take brings tranquility and peace into your body. Imagine that as you exhale, the air carries your tension and anxiety. Try saying to yourself, "Breathing in serenity and calm," as you take a breath. Saying, "breathing out tension and anxiety" as you exhale. Ten minutes of breath focus is a reasonable initial objective. Add time gradually until your workouts last roughly 15 to 20 minutes.

Body scan. A body scan is a relaxing technique that combines imagery and breath focus. You can use this method to improve your body awareness and understanding of the relationship between your mind and body. Almost everyone has muscular tension that is unneeded. Where we each sense it, though, varies. A lady can have a tight neck and shoulders while her spouse has a band of iron pressing into his forehead. You can find the stress in your body using a body scan and then release it. A body scan is a rather easy procedure. Pay attention to one body part at a time. Imagine that muscle in your thoughts as you do this. Imagine it to be welcoming, pleasant, and informal. Any tension will vanish. Use these guidelines as a guide:

- Lie down or sit. Focus on your breath first. Breathe deeply, feeling your tummy rise with each inhalation and descend with each exhalation. Before you begin, breathe in this manner for two minutes.

- Pay close attention to your right big toe. Concentrate on the space between each atom as you see the atoms in your toe. Imagine that your toe is relaxed, warm, and open.

- Now turn your attention to your right foot's other toes, picturing each individually. Once more, please pay attention to how your toes feel and try to imagine them being open, warm, and at ease.

- Gradually turn your attention to your foot, mentally traveling from the ball to the arch and then the top of the foot.

- Pay close attention to your ankle, calf, knee, thigh, and hip as you work your way up your leg at this point. Spend some time going through each section slowly. Imagine the atoms and the space between them for each body part. Imagine that every muscle is warm, open, and relaxed.

● ● Permit your right leg to unwind and sag into the floor's support.

● Rehearse these motions now, concentrating on your left foot and leg.

● Next, pay attention to your back. Is it constricting or tense? Please pay close attention to every vertebra and the region around it. Feel free and roomy in each vertebra. Relax each back muscle as you slowly work your way there.

● Then, gradually move on to your chest and abdomen. Imagine your internal organs and the area in between them. Feel free to let your belly feel open and light.

● ● Focus on your right thumb first, then the rest of your fingers. Imagine each finger individually, then slowly relax your palm, wrist, forearm, elbow, upper arm, and shoulder as you move down your hand and arm.

● Experience a warm, airy, and light sensation in your right arm.

● Repeat the process with your left arm and hand.

● Consider your mouth and neck. Yawn. Working through your jaw, eyes, and forehead, let your entire face relax. Focus on the top and back of your head now.

- Sink completely into your chair or bed. Does it have a calm, light sensitivity to it? Observe your breathing. Take a moment to relax and take a deep breath. Imagine releasing any pent-up stress from your body as you exhale.

- If you still feel tightness in any part of your body, concentrate on your breathing and let it out as you exhale.

- Spend a few minutes sitting or lying down and pay attention to how expansive and light your body feels. Then slowly open your eyes. If you feel like stretching, do so now.

Guided imaginary. A powerful method of inducing the relaxation response is guided imagery, often known as visualization. The scenes, locations, or experiences you select enhance the feeling of inner tranquility. They sever the flow of routine cognition. Even while imaging is frequently promoted as helpful for patients with cancer and other illnesses, there isn't enough research to back up some health-improving claims. However, it has been demonstrated to decrease the unpleasant side effects of many medications, including chemotherapy. A therapist may speak soothing descriptions of white sand beaches, gurgling streams, and flower-filled meadows, or they may be recorded on a CD to aid in visualization. Make sure the visual is calming; otherwise, the activity won't work. For instance, if you have hay sickness, you can associate a field of flowers with unpleasant memories. If you're not using a CD, visualize your space and pretend it's where you are. What scents do you detect: vanilla in a kitchen, rain boiling off the scorching pavement, or pine needles? Do you hear anything? What's moving, clouds or birds? Take in the hues of your surroundings. Pay attention to the senses, such as a chilly breeze on your cheek, gravel under your feet, or the aroma of flowering trees. If you believe it would be useful to you in locating this location once more, record yourself describing everything. Find a calm area to sit in before beginning your guided imagery session. Put your body in a relaxed position. Spend a few minutes clearing your thoughts while taking slow, even breaths, and then visualize the soothing visuals. Passively accept bothersome thoughts by watching them. Then come back to the sensory web. Spend 10 to 20 minutes exercising.

Nutrition. The phrase "garbage in, garbage out," famous in the computer age, refers to much more than only software development. Your dietary decisions might increase your stress levels or reduce them by nourishing your body. Your diet has a significant impact on your risk of contracting a variety of diseases, including cancer, diabetes, heart disease, and hypertension, all of which have an effect on your general level of stress. Overeating-related obesity is also associated with a variety of conditions. Millions of Americans constantly reminded of their failure to reach the slender look admired in modern culture find it a source of stress.

Additionally, undernourishment can be a problem, especially for older individuals. In America, most older men and women lack sufficient amounts of calcium, zinc, iron, magnesium, folic acid, and the vitamins B6, B12, and D. Your mood, mental clarity, bones, heart, and vitality are all impacted by these nutrients. Such nutritional deficiencies also have effects on stress. For many people, food represents much more than just nutrition. Some people use food to soothe worry or to fill a hole in their emotions. On the other hand, eating can be a source of anxiety for people with eating disorders.

Maintaining your energy level is greatly aided by giving your body the proper kinds of meals in the right proportions.

During breakfast: Lean proteins, whole grains, and fruits should all be combined. Good choices are two pieces of whole-grain toast with fresh fruit and skim milk or a glass of skim milk with a serving of oats topped with half a cup of fresh blueberries. A bowl of whole-grain cereal and low-fat plain yogurt with berries are also options.

Lunch and dinner: Use your plate as a reference point. Vegetables, either fresh or cooked, should fill half of it. Lean protein, such as chicken, turkey, fish, beans, lentils, or tofu, should make up the other quarter of the diet, with whole grains making up the first quarter.

When you snack: Instead of munching straight from the box, portion out a dish that is the right size and consume that. Be careful not to expose yourself to temptation. Instead of keeping cartons of ice cream in the fridge, stock it with healthy snacks like fresh fruit and vegetables. Then, when you're genuinely in the mood for ice cream, go get a scoop.

In conclusion:

✓ Use smaller plates instead of large ones, which encourage larger portions.

✓ Refrain from getting seconds; take a piece of fruit if you're still hungry after the meal.

✓ Have a hot beverage, like tea, soup, or broth, before your meal. You can avoid overeating by choosing hot drinks over cold ones because they are more filling.

✓ Before having a snack, take a deep breath and consider whether you are hungry or your desire to eat is driven by fear, boredom, or loneliness. Find another way to unwind if you're feeling overwhelmed, such as taking a stroll or calling a friend. To check if it satisfies you, attempt to sip on a glass of water.

Instead of adding to your stress about how well or poorly you eat, consider making a few small adjustments to your diet. Could you raise the amount of fruit and veggies you consume each day? Could you broaden your color pallet by incorporating a variety of deep-hued fruits and vegetables, which typically have higher antioxidant and nutritional content? Could you substitute some bad fats, like those in meat, cheese, and most commercial baked goods, with healthier ones, such as nuts and cold-water fish like salmon and olive or canola oil? Could you consciously choose healthy grains like brown rice, barley, quinoa, and whole-wheat couscous more frequently than refined grains like white rice or white flour? These simple steps can have a real impact on your health. Food provides nutrients as well as comfort and pleasure.

However, eating fast food while swerving lanes on the motorway provides none of these advantages. Our culture is rushed, and it impacts how we eat. Fast food has supplanted family meals, and eating while driving has become such a part of a culture that the term "dashboard dining" has been created to characterize it. But the issue with eating quickly and hurriedly is that you might consume more than you intended, not to mention indigestion that will almost certainly occur. Your appreciation of eating can be revived by taking the time to eat slowly and deliberately. Since the "fullness signal" in the brain doesn't start to activate until 20 minutes after eating, it will also help you control how much food you eat. This implies that if you devour a meal, you can complete it before you even start to feel full. Instead, make an effort to slow down and enjoy each meal. Set a space for yourself and take a seat before you begin to eat mindfully. For a few seconds, close your eyes and take a few deep breaths in and out to help you concentrate. Give the situation your complete attention. Before tasting your food, examine it and take in its flavors. Chew carefully to enjoy the flavors and sensations. Don't swallow quickly to go on to the next mouthful. By engaging your senses, you may improve your taste for more nutritious, fresh meals and end the cycle of stress eating. Consider how you feel before you start eating, during the meal, and after. Are you hungry, or is it just "time" for dinner? Do you eat to relieve stress? You might discover that other stress-reduction methods are just as enjoyable as eating as you learn to recognize and understand your feelings.

Exercise. Almost all forms of exercise, when done frequently and with moderate intensity, offer a variety of health-improving advantages. Exercise boosts the immune system, decreases blood pressure, maintains bones strong and healthy, and improves cholesterol levels. Additionally, it improves your mood and metabolism, allowing you to age with vigor and independence. According to research, many of these advantages are offered even by so-called lifestyle hobbies like gardening or playing physical games with kids. There are various ways that exercise can be used to prevent stress from building up. Running away from an approaching bus, for example, can help you exercise right after the stress reaction kicks in and release stress hormones the way nature intended. Motion in almost any form helps release accumulated muscle tension. As well as repetitive workouts like walking, running, or rowing, other hobbies like yoga, tai chi, or qi gong can cause a relaxation response. You can combat daily stress by partaking in these kinds of activities regularly. Try to change your focus while exercising to become aware of yourself, your feelings, and your surroundings to maximize the benefits of stress alleviation. You ought to feel more at ease and in the moment after reading this. Resistance training can also make use of this strategy. Coordinate your breathing with your movements as you raise and lower the weights, and as you carry out each exercise, pay close attention to how your body feels. A few sage pieces of advice are necessary:

✓ Consult your doctor before starting any exercise program if you are not typically active, have health issues, or suffer from a painful or incapacitating condition.

✓ Pay attention to your body when you exercise. Use only the motions that feel natural to you. Gradually increase your range as you get more robust or more flexible.

✓ Incorporate deep, relaxing breathing throughout your daily routine. It could be most straightforward for you to start by getting comfortable with the movements of the exercises you choose before adding deep breathing.

✓ Join a class led by a qualified instructor if you want to attempt yoga, tai chi, or qi gong so they can assist you in learning the proper motions and modify the routine to suit your needs.

The following exercises are perfect for inducing relaxation. Consider incorporating some or all of these tasks into your daily routine.

Yoga. It is based on Indian philosophy and is a great approach to increasing body awareness and triggering relaxation responses. These fundamental components, pranayamas (rhythmic breathing), meditation, and asanas, are present in all forms of yoga (stretching postures). Yoga, like tai chi and qi gong, improves tranquility while increasing flexibility and coordination. Another potential advantage for yoga practitioners was discovered in a 2005 lifestyle and health practices research. Over ten years, middle-aged adults with average weight who practiced yoga for four or more years gained three pounds less than those who did not. Over the same time frame, overweight people who consistently practiced yoga dropped an average of 5 pounds. The study's authors proposed two additional explanations for this impact because yoga is typically not energetic enough for this effect to be attributable to increased calorie expenditure. Yoga may have cellular effects on weight regulation because it reduces cortisol levels in the body, a stress hormone. High cortisol levels have been linked to the expanding waistline that frequently comes with middle age. Another hypothesis is that the mindfulness developed via yoga promotes a greater awareness of one's body, a mental state that transfers into better food and exercise behaviors.

Tai chi. This set of circular, leisurely movements has its roots in martial arts. Elderly folks significantly benefit from tai chi. It guards against a progressive deterioration in physical function by strengthening balance, muscle strength, and aerobic capacity, which helps prevent falls that can result in fractures. Tai chi reduces the chance of falling by almost half in men and women at least 70 years old. Another randomized research of sedentary persons aged 60 or older found that low-intensity movements result in drops in blood pressure, similar to those attained with moderate-intensity aerobics. Some doctors suggest tai chi for those with osteoarthritis to enhance the range of motion and lessen joint swelling.

Qi gong. Breathing, meditation, mild exercise, and flowing movements are all combined in this ancient Chinese technique. The Chinese phrase for the life force said to flow through the body is qi or chi. The purpose of qi gong is to unblock and balance the qi flow. Regular practice helps reduce your heart rate, blood pressure, and oxygen consumption. Each of these outcomes is a part of the relaxation response. Additionally, Qi gong may improve flexibility and balance.

Rhythmic activity. Walking, jogging, swimming, or cycling are all rhythmic exercises that can be soothing and relaxing. Once you start, pay attention to how your breathing supports the movement. Repeat the concentration word, phrase, or prayer you've chosen as you breathe rhythmically. Don't forget to take a passive stance. When distracting thoughts arise, gradually shift your attention to breathing and movement.

Mindful walk. An excellent example of exercise with relaxation in mind is going for a mindful walk. Be mindful of your body's sensations as you breathe regularly and move your body. What sensations do you have as air enters your nose and exits through your mouth? Gradually open your eyes and nose to your surroundings' sights and smells. Take note of the just-mowed grass, flowers, trees, leaves on the ground, dappled sunlight, or gray clouds. How does the air outside feel when it touches your body? How does the ground feel and sound under your feet? What is going through your mind right now? A calm, deliberate walk might help you relax and find your core. Instead, a faster speed that tests your limits can be peaceful and exhilarating. In this instance, pay closer attention to your bodily sensations, such as your accelerated breathing and heartbeat, and how your muscles react when you exert them.

Social support. People gain when social buffers soften the inevitable knocks and bruises of life, much as a ship is protected by the rubber bumpers that keep it from a hard wooden dock. Studies demonstrate a considerable protective effect of social links on health and happiness, at least those that represent positive interactions. Researchers in Sweden who followed more than 17,000 men and women for six years discovered that individuals who felt the most isolation and loneliness were nearly four times more likely to die young than those with strong social networks. Lack of strong social and communal ties increased the risk of dying about two to three times, according to California researchers who followed 7,000 inhabitants of Alameda County for nine years. A supportive social network is woven by confidants, friends, acquaintances, coworkers, relatives, and spouses or partners. Their assistance could be direct, or it could be mainly emotional. Studies demonstrate that those with more social support perform better on immune function tests when exposed to various stresses, such as caregiving, surgery, exams, and job strain. The number of natural killer cells, which can eliminate virus-laden cells and specific tumor cells, was higher in breast cancer patients who felt they had high-quality emotional support from an intimate relationship, social support from a doctor, and nourishment from other connections than in patients who did not. It should come as no surprise that relationship quality matters. According to research, negative ones, such as a troubled marriage or a taxing caregiving arrangement, may be more damaging than beneficial.

Given the benefits and joys of social connections, why not seize opportunities to widen your social network and strengthen the relationships you already have? Here are several methods for carrying it out:

- If you often wait for someone to contact you, pick up the phone and make an approach.

- Look into some of the numerous volunteer options, from employing tools to improve affordable housing to mentoring young people or businesspeople. Search for opportunities that match your skills and interests on VolunteerMatch (www.volunteermatch.org), Senior Corps (www.seniorcorps.org), or by contacting the United Way in your area.

- Take advantage of technology's softer side. Your global reach is expanded by telephones and email. Free online time and assistance with setting up a free email account may be available from libraries and senior centers.

- Discover like-minded individuals by enrolling in engaging classes and organizations.

- If it's difficult for you to attend religious services, ask other attendees to accompany you. If a severe sickness prevents you from attending, find out if your spiritual leader visits people in their homes.

- Social assistance works both ways. Offer your friends, family, and neighbors your help, and accept it when it is extended to you.

- Express your confidence. A close friendship may develop even further if this is done.

- You might want to adopt a pet. Pets can improve your emotional and physical well-being, according to research.

- Seek assistance if social anxiety, phobia, or sadness prevents you from connecting with others. Consult your physician beforehand. Therapy, medication, or a combination have helped many people.

Nurturing yourself. Another crucial step in stress management is learning to take care of oneself. Even though you may be an expert at taking care of others, attending to your own needs might not come naturally to you. For instance, it is accepted wisdom that women spend more of their waking hours tending to others than men. Studies indicate that women spend more time than males tending to the home and their loved ones, whether or not they have jobs outside the home. If you're a woman, chances are good that you act as the emotional binder that binds marriages and families. You purchase the greeting cards, answer the phone to offer assistance when someone is ill, and handle a sizable portion of the work or service coordination required to look after aged parents, children, grandchildren, and spouses who require care. You're expected to be selfless in our culture. Your needs might be neglected, and putting your needs first is viewed as selfish. In our society, males are encouraged to advance in their careers. That might motivate someone to give their job their full attention at the expense of other interests. Men are deterred from fostering their nurturing side in this way. Men are pushed toward receiving, just as women are pressured from the start to give to others. Due to these imbalances, both sexes may experience distress. You might not feel confident taking some time to relax if you're a woman. If you're a man, you might not have much experience developing your own caring rituals, and you could feel uncomfortable doing so, just like your female counterpart. Learning to focus on oneself in healthy, rejuvenating ways has advantages for both men and women. There is no one method for practicing self-care. Instead, it's a guiding principle for your entire existence. The spark you develop by fostering your creativity, job, relationships, sexuality, or spiritual side magnifies the therapeutic impact of other stress-relieving methods. The numerous, diverse alternatives for nurturing oneself include:

✓ journal writing

✓ cognitive restructuring

✓ relaxation exercises

✓ affirmations and prayer

✓ social support

✓ creative, productive, and leisure activities.

Consider how these strategies and self-nurturing actions work as dry seeds for a garden. Those that do more than just scratch the ground, throw some seeds in and stand back to watch what grows are rewarded with lush growth. Dig \sdeep. Drink plenty of water.

When necessary, get rid of the plot's suffocating weeds. What you reap can be significantly influenced by the depth of your prior experiences, your willingness to step beyond your comfort zone, and desire to live a courageous, loving, and joyful life.

Daily "to-do" lists might drain energy due to their nerve-wracking pressure. Even if the addition involves leisure, creativity, or quality time with a loved one, adding additional items to the list could make you feel more displeased than excited. But when you rejuvenate yourself in ways that are important to you, you increase your supply of vigor and happiness. How would you define "creativity"? Creating a quick story? Clay sculpture? Organizing a retreat? Pulling out a paint container? Dancing throughout the space? Creating a deck? Prepare a feast? Designing a garden? Find small and large ways to carry out your dreams if you have any that you haven't yet investigated.

Sing in the shower, learn from an expert, or perform for your friends. Join a class you think you'd like if you don't know where to start. Give yourself a chance to experiment with several choices. If the first one doesn't hold your attention or if the outcomes of your efforts fall short of what you had hoped for, don't give up. Find your favorite creative endeavor and pursue it. Productive work creates connections with others and the wider world and gives life purpose. Whether these duties are paid, volunteer or garden work doesn't matter. They provide enjoyment and, occasionally, the opportunity for creativity. If you are retired or feel that the job that pays the bills doesn't give many opportunities for fulfillment, locate another place to exercise your industrious side. If you approach anything carefully, the simplest activity, like chopping vegetables for dinner or mopping the floor, may become less tedious and more enjoyable. Working with others might lead to connections that can help you grow in other ways. Working for the good of others frequently provides unique satisfaction. These volunteer opportunities are available to persons of all ages and abilities. Find volunteer opportunities in your area by contacting local groups. Time management is a task that many of us find particularly difficult.

Spending time reading a book, playing tennis, taking a hot bath, or meditating for 30 minutes may seem selfish. The likelihood of receiving approving nods increases with productive and even creative endeavors. So take a snooze while sprawled out in a hammock. Take a massage. Set aside 20 minutes during your hectic day to focus on breathing or perform a body scan. Take in the music's tones that you find relaxing, energizing, or enjoyable. By scheduling this time for yourself, you can prevent weariness and burnout and be better able to concentrate and behave more amicably while doing your daily chores. Think of it as a present you give yourself that benefits others as well.

Relieving stress through writing. You've probably learned to suppress "inappropriate" feelings like anger, fear, annoyance, and grief if you're like most people. Of course, the cap can come off occasionally. These feelings then burst forth with great intensity, though perhaps not in the best way. Writing in a journal is a secure way to express any emotion, even the most upsetting, frightful, or depressing ones. A pen and a blank paper can provide great relief and perhaps even reveal buried problems. Psychotherapist James W. Pennebaker, who started researching this topic in the late 1970s, claims that writing about traumatic experiences can also positively affect the body. One group of participants was asked to write down their most intense sensations and thoughts regarding the most horrific event they could recall for several research. In a control group, only unimportant occurrences were mentioned. For four days, each group wrote for 15 minutes each day. In one study, those who expressed intense feelings said they felt better, and for nearly half a year following, they had much fewer doctor visits and disease symptoms. In a related trial, those who expressed strong emotions had more active T cells, immune system defenses, for the following six weeks. Journal writing is beneficial for persons with asthma and arthritis, according to additional studies. Why does writing about sensitive topics affect one's mental and physical health? According to Pennebaker, expressing suppressed emotions decreases the stress that would otherwise raise blood pressure, heart rate, and muscle tension. Just a little suggestion before you get started:

- It is better to discuss really upsetting incidents and circumstances with a skilled therapist, such as domestic violence, rape, or direct exposure to acts of terrorism or war. In other events, you can handle things independently and only need expert aid if you feel you need it.
- If you're in good physical health, decide which of your present problems or events is the most distressing. It's usually one that you think about a lot. Or, if you believe that your current issues are the result of previous circumstances, write about distressing times in your life.
- Truly release. Please write down your thoughts and the reasons behind them.
- Not for readers, but for yourself. Sentence structure and grammar are unimportant. Feel free to repeat yourself if you run out of things to say in the allowed time.
- Perform this practice for 15 to 20 minutes every day for

three to four days or for up to a week if you think writing is still beneficial.

You're not limited to writing about stressors. Another strategy is to keep a thankfulness notebook or a journal to brainstorm ideas to make your life more joyful and meaningful. To complete this activity, dedicate 10 minutes each day to writing in your journal about any happy happenings in your life. Maybe it had a child, landing a dream job, seeing the French countryside, or earning a doctorate. Pay attention to your feelings both now and then. Consider your feelings for a while after you've finished writing. Did you feel pleased about a victory that you fought for? Thrilled about a novel encounter? Flooded with acceptance and love as a result of a relationship with a loved one? Find ways to relive those emotions right now. Can you think of any prospects that would give you those same emotions right now?

Cognitive reorganization. Take time to reflect on the ideas going through your mind as you prepare for work this morning. What did you tell yourself? What were you contemplating? Then consider your feelings. Perhaps a straightforward concept, like "the train is late," suddenly got out of hand. You suddenly had the thought, "I'll be late for work. I won't arrive at my appointment in time. My manager will be upset with me. My employment is in danger. Even seemingly positive thoughts can sometimes spiral out of control. I wonder how good that lab is? From "Wonderful, the lab report shows my biopsy results are negative!" can happen very rapidly. It's possible that the outcomes were favorable, but the lab missed them. Cancer that is not discovered worsens. It can already be too late if the issue is discovered too late. These instances serve as illustrations of automatic thought. Nearly as easily as a growling Doberman running in your direction, they can cause a stress response. The constant stream of unfavorable ideas that many individuals experience is similar to the automatic switchover of negative thoughts that many people have in response to particular people or circumstances. The phrases "I look dreadful," "I can't do this," "I'm stupid," "I'm such a screw-up," and "I'm a loser" are common examples. The voice may come from you or another person, such as an overbearing parent. This inner critic can make you miserable and stressed even when there aren't any overtly stressful events. The foundation of cognitive therapy is the idea that attitudes and perceptions influence feelings and moods. Depression and anxiety may be exacerbated by a constant stream of extremely negative thoughts. These negative ideas frequently contain illogical exaggerations and distortions. But once you master the techniques of cognitive restructuring, a cognitive therapy method that aids people in altering their thinking, they can be dissected and deflated.

Below are listed ten typical cognitive distortions. Which of these distortions appeals to you the most? Please use this list to become more conscious of your ingrained negative thought patterns and try to replace them with more sensible, optimistic ones.

✓ *All or nothing.* Nothing is gray; everything is either black or white. You view yourself as a complete failure if your performance is less than perfect.

✓ *Overgeneralization.* One bad experience, like experiencing your spouse's abuse or coming across a dubious business, is a continuation of a never-ending string of unfortunate situations and failures. You might think, for instance, "He's usually frigid" or "Nobody is trustworthy."

✓ *Mental filter.* Like a drop of food coloring in a glass of water, one unpleasant incident, like a nasty remark made to you during an otherwise enjoyable evening, casts a shadow over everything. It appears you have filtered all the light and can only see blackness.

✓ *Ignoring the positive.* Positive feedback, such as a tender gesture or overt praise, isn't considered. All accolades are met with self-deprecation from you. It's not a huge deal, you might say.

✓ *Jumping to a conclusion.* You jump to unfavorable judgments without investigating whether they are supported by facts. "My friend seems disturbed; she must be mad at me," you might be mind-reading. Or you can be telling fortunes: "I just know my medical test results won't be good."

✓ *Magnification or minimization.* You overstate prospective issues or errors until they assume the dimensions of a disaster. Or you downplay everything that would make you feel good, like gratitude for a decent deed you performed or the understanding that other people have defects.

✓ *Emotional thinking.* You believe that your unpleasant feelings are a reflection of the situation. "I feel inferior," for instance. I must not be as good as others as a result.

✓ *"Should" components.* You follow a strict set of ideals and internal guidelines for what you "should" be doing, and you feel bad when you don't follow them.

✓ *Labeling.* You refer to yourself unfavorably instead of describing a mistake or difficulty in your life: "I'm a screw-up." When someone else's actions annoy you, you generalize about them, saying things like, "She's so controlling."

✓ *Personalization.* You hold yourself accountable for starting a bad thing that happened for complicated reasons or for something that was mostly beyond your control. "I never would have developed cancer if I had cared for myself."

You can recognize skewed thinking with the use of other cues. Using the words "must," "should," "ought," "always," and "never" in sentences makes them more severe than they need to be and shows inflexible thinking that could use some bending. Some of the above distortions are likely recognizable if you're like most people. The second stage challenges any straightforward, unfavorable ideas that stress you out needlessly. Naturally, it's easy when the thoughts are blatantly false, like "I never do anything well." It is more difficult when simple lies are blended with elements of truth, as in the statement, "At my age, I know I'll never achieve my goals." That might be true if you've always wanted to be a well-known opera singer but haven't had the time or the skills to make it happen for a single objective. You might probably include other objectives that you did accomplish, though. And if you scaled back your dream by realizing that you enjoy singing, whether the Metropolitan Opera audience is riveted to your every word, you might even strike off on a new track and succeed in it. One strategy for reducing the stress that results from distortions and negative thoughts is the four-step procedure that the BensonHenry Institute for Mind Body Medicine teaches:

- *Stop.* Decide to take a mental break. Say "Stop" if you feel stressed out going forward. This effectively halts the negative stress loop.
- *Breathe.* Take a few deep breaths to ease your body's stress and promote relaxation.
- *Reflect.* Consider the following inquiries for yourself: Is this idea or opinion accurate? Did I make a hasty judgment? What genuine proof do I have? Am I allowing my bad thoughts to grow? Exists a different perspective on the situation? What is the worst that might occur? Does my style of thinking benefit me?
- *Choose.* Choose a strategy for addressing the cause of your stress. If distortion is the cause of the issue, examine your assumptions and revise how you perceive reality. Consider the following inquiries for yourself: How else might I consider this? What more can I do to manage my stress better? Remember that most of the things we worry about never happen.

It takes practice to restructure bad beliefs and distortions. You don't have to pretend to be happy or disregard reality. It is frequently possible to change your perspective by paying more attention to the good than the bad. Other times, you can face a difficult reality without losing sight of the bigger, better picture. For instance, you could say instead of "I should be practicing relaxation response techniques every day," "I want to practice relaxation response techniques every day," or "I feel calmer and happier when I routinely practice relaxation response techniques." Encourage yourself to keep finding time rather than criticizing yourself for falling short. Recognizing this without allowing it to consume you may be helpful when a disease flares up and leaves you feeling helpless. Substitute "I feel unwell and in agony, today" for "I'll never get any better." I can use various drugs and methods to lessen my suffering. I'll probably feel better the following week and be able to continue with my regular program. A friend's insight on a dilemma or issue that appears intractable can frequently be helpful. They might spot a critical mistake in your reasoning that you have missed. Instead of worrying about the case, it might be beneficial to divert your attention from it. Try a little meditation or use visualization to relax. Attend a mind/body program or get assistance from a qualified mental health practitioner competent in cognitive restructuring if distortions are especially challenging or deeply established.

It could be beneficial to structure your worrying by designating a specific time or location where you can "hold" your anxieties. Using these tactics, you can prevent negative thoughts and fears from permeating your days. Call a timeout for yourself if your thoughts are racing, you're feeling stressed or overwhelmed, or you're having trouble focusing. Write down your worries, then set a timer for 15 minutes. But when the buzzer goes off, put your concerns aside and practice being truly present. Accept your worries and anxieties without passing judgment. This task might benefit from mindfulness meditation practice. If your anxiety is persistent and you are going through a trying moment, such as a divorce or a financial setback, you might find it helpful to set aside a specified period each day to write down your fears.

The "goose in the bottle" practice might help you reframe your thoughts when you make snap judgments or linger on the bad. The practice is based on a well-known Zen koan that challenges us to think of a way to extricate a goose from a glass bottle. A gosling is put in a bottle by a man and fed via the bottle's neck until it is completely grown and the bottle is full, at which point the official begs the Zen master to evaluate the issue.

Positive psychology. The American Psychological Association has acknowledged positive psychology as an emerging science, and many professionals who create stress-management programs use its ideas. It focuses on identifying and advancing the elements that enable people to prosper. Instead of focusing on the causes of sadness, a study in this area examines the components of a happy existence. It considers the impact of characteristics like optimism, humor, and even eccentricity. For instance, optimists typically perform better than pessimists when dealing with stressful circumstances. They are more likely to find ways to make the best of stressful situations, look for ways to make the best of stressful situations, and employ problem-solving techniques to deal with challenges. According to several studies, optimists frequently experience superior physical health. Over 30 years, a large-scale study including more than 830 individuals discovered that those classed as pessimists had a 19% higher chance of mortality than those who were optimists.

Additionally, a 10-year study involving 1,300 men found that optimism may shield older men from heart disease. A 2007 study of 2,900 healthy people revealed that those who reported positive emotions had reduced cortisol levels, one of the stress chemicals that may be linked to high blood pressure and weakened immune system performance. In addition, C-reactive protein and interleukin-6 levels were lower in women with positive outlooks. High levels of these substances may be linked to type 2 diabetes and atherosclerosis, a buildup of fatty deposits in arteries that can result in heart attacks and strokes. This information might make you even more pessimistic if you're not naturally an optimist. Stop letting it. Relax by taking a big breath.

There is evidence that preventing pessimism is more crucial than increasing optimism. Some people are indeed naturally optimistic, but it's also true that emotional maturity is largely a product of nurture. Your current perspective and behaviors may improve with practice. You may have already experimented with some positive psychology practices. They emphasize the value of close relationships, cognitive retraining, and journaling. Other methods enable people to access their sense of thanksgiving, gratitude, or humor. These treatment strategies all center on enhancing the good. Various happiness activities were shown to be particularly efficient in raising happiness and lowering depressive symptoms in a study that evaluated the effects of several different happiness exercises. Martin Seligman, director of the University of Pennsylvania Positive Psychology Center and a pioneer in the field of positive psychology, was one of the researchers who gave 577 adults the option of participating in one of five happiness exercises or receiving a placebo (writing down their earliest memories every night for a week). Before and after the workouts, the subjects completed two surveys: a happiness index and a depression scale. For up to six months, two of these exercises, "Using signature strengths in a new way" and "Three good things," increased happiness and decreased depressive symptoms. After giving the individuals one week to complete these exercises, the researchers found that those who kept up with them independently experienced better, more long-lasting outcomes. The best initial results came from another activity called "Gratitude Visit," which significantly reduced depression symptoms and raised happiness scores. However, the effects vanished after three months. See the "Boost your happiness" section for instructions on carrying out these activities. There has also been a lot of fascinating research on comedy. Laughter has been shown to increase immune system function and decrease levels of stress chemicals like cortisol and adrenaline in the body. It makes sense why many mental-physical practitioners advise laughing. They frequently advise patients to watch hilarious movies, read funny books, and accept absurdity in everyday life.

Chapter four

The many forms of stress

———

Each person has a unique perspective on what stresses them out and how they respond. However, several general challenges affect us all. Are you a man or a woman? What age are you? Do you have a job? Or do you aspire to be? Are you taking care of an old or ill family member? The various facets of stress are examined in this section.

Everyone's stress response has similar physiology. However, some researchers think that how stress is felt and handled by men and women differs significantly.

In community surveys conducted in many countries, women consistently report more distress than men. According to a study published in the Journal of Personality and Social Psychology involving roughly 1,100 American adults, women are more likely than men to experience ongoing stress and feel as though they have no control over their lives. Why the difference? According to some researchers, the social responsibilities that women typically shoulder, such as child care, elder care, and housework, expose them to more opportunities for distress. The "second shift" for women who work outside the home is made up of these duties. This added burden has been linked to long-term health issues, as was shown in a significant study of nurses. Over four years, there was an increased risk of heart attacks or other manifestations of coronary artery disease for the women in the study who provided nine or more hours per week of care for a disabled or chronically ill spouse. Contrarily, men report financial stress more frequently than women, which makes sense given that men are traditionally expected to be the breadwinners. Another study asked 166 married couples to keep a daily journal for six weeks, recording 21 typical stressors like fights and workloads at home and work. Wives had 5% higher odds than husbands of reporting "any distress" days and had 19% higher odds of experiencing "high-distress" days. The women reported encountering more stressful situations, even though they did not frequently carry feelings of "high distress" from one day to the next. Certain demands had a greater impact on men or women.

For instance, men reacted more strongly to arguments with children, financial hardships, or work overload, whereas women were more upset by arguments with spouses, transportation issues, or family obligations. The researchers propose that the behavior may have had evolutionary advantages for women and that sex hormone and the pituitary hormone oxytocin are partially to blame for such differences. Oxytocin promotes relaxation and reduces anxiety. Male sex hormones have the opposite effect on it as female sex hormones do. Men and women both release adrenaline and cortisol during stressful situations, and men also release testosterone, which tends to increase hostility and aggression. For women, who are typically smaller than men, may be pregnant, or are caring for young children, the impulse to fight or flee in the face of danger could have disastrous results. The possibility that "tend-and-befriend" might benefit women is an intriguing one to consider. Social connections are essential for minimizing the negative effects of stress, after all.

Does aging affect how stressed out you are? Significant life events, like the death of a spouse, an illness, or an accident, are more likely to affect you over time. Heart disease, arthritis, and cancer are three conditions more prevalent in older people and major causes of pain and disability. Unpleasant daily realities can result from the side effects of prescription drugs and other treatments. In later life, sleep disturbances are also typical. These can all, or any one of them, cause stress. You may become more of an introvert than you'd like to be due to a declining interest in exercise, which may be brought on by osteoporosis or deteriorating vision, hearing, and balance as you age. A cycle of deteriorating physical capabilities and growing frailty may result from this. Is that demanding? Just ask anyone who struggles to complete simple household tasks or worries that walking outside could result in broken bones. People can adapt to changing abilities, but getting there may not be easy.

Additionally, cultural training might have an impact. Older people were raised in a time when showing emotion was discouraged. Many older women never develop the skills necessary to express needs clearly, handle uncomfortable conflicts before they become a source of stress, or have many opportunities to work outside the home, which can provide some women with creative and productive outlets. However, many people find solace in their religious beliefs, which may impact their health and longevity. According to some preliminary research, changes in the HPA axis, which regulates the stress response, may exacerbate specific common health issues in older people, like cardiovascular disease and stroke. Both aging and chronic stress may cause these disturbances in some people. Continuous exposure to stress hormones, such as cortisol, can damage hippocampus nerve cells, which may impact how learning and memory are processed. Thankfully, not all of these effects are unavoidable. There is a good chance that you can deal with significant stressors in your life once you identify them. It is possible to stop or at least slow physical deterioration and some age-related illnesses through exercise, a healthy diet, the right medications, and stress management techniques. Try the "Tips for reducing stress in older adults" link at the left.

Giving to others satisfies a fundamental social contract in ways that can bind generations and people together. Undoubtedly, providing care for an elderly parent or a sick spouse is a worthwhile and frequently fulfilling endeavor. But it's not simple. Being a caregiver can cause stress, exhaustion, anger, guilt, grief, and other challenging emotions to surface frequently. The majority of caregivers are female. Women in the so-called sandwich generation, who are simultaneously caring for children and elderly parents and may also be working outside the home, have a challenging time with this task. While tending to others' needs, your well-being could deteriorate. Studies on men and women who provide long-term care for kin have found that caregivers have higher rates of illness, suppressed immune responses, slower healing, and even higher mortality rates. It would help if you had time for yourself and your family and support, stress relief, and support to provide care. The "Tips for managing caregiver stress" at the left could be helpful.

American workers now put in more hours than they did in earlier decades. Cell phones, telecommuting, email, and fax machines have broken the line separating work and play. Employee anxiety is fueled by repeated threats of layoffs and the exodus of industries to countries where labor is less expensive. The employment of older workers may be in danger from younger aspirants who are knowledgeable about new technologies or simply less expensive to a company. Anxiety is also fueled by a generally unsteady economy and rising food and gas prices. Does this picture indicate a rise in workplace stress? Being confident is challenging. According to some researchers, the scales used to measure workplace stress may be too limited to be accurate for people in various occupations and aren't always relevant to modern working methods.

Additionally, positive changes like the abolition of some dirty, boring jobs and the expansion of opportunities in difficult new fields typically receive little attention. The advantages to one's mental health also apply to work. Then, a more appropriate query would be, "How does your job affect you?" Does it enthrall and energize you, or does it drain you? Do you feel satisfied? Do you receive the help you require to perform your job? How much power do you actually have over what you do? According to a study of nearly 21,300 female registered nurses, those who reported having little social support at work, high job demands, and little job control were more likely to be in poor health when data collection began.

Regardless of how you feel about your job, there are techniques you can use to reduce stress whenever it arises. Try the "Tips for managing work-related stress" first on the left. Working can be stressful, but so can not working. People who are unemployed or retired might find it challenging to respond to the frequently asked question, "What do you do?" Even stay-at-home moms can experience anxiety over it. Too often, people's societal positions are determined by their jobs. Stereotypes are evoked by terms like "stay-at-home mom," "retired," and "laid off." Another factor is the financial burden of not working or working in a job that doesn't pay. These stressors can be overcome in a variety of ways. You can better control both realistic and irrational fears by addressing cognitive distortions. You can reduce your stress by relaxing and taking care of yourself. Additionally, bookstores offer a wealth of career advice, from finding the job you love to acing job interviews. Remember that there is a life outside work where you can find fulfillment and opportunity.

Chapter five

How stress affects the body

———

Numerous studies indicate that prolonged stress can have negative effects on your body. Heart disease and high blood pressure are influenced by chronic stress. It might also weaken the immune system, affecting asthma, gastrointestinal issues, cancer, and ulcers. The widely held belief that high-stress levels somehow hasten age is also supported by new research. In fact, the stress of caring for sick children caused these women to age on a cellular level more quickly than the mothers of healthy children who made up the control group, according to a 2004 study that followed mothers of these mothers. Telomeres, which act as protective caps on the ends of chromosomes during cell division, gradually get shorter with each replication. The stressed caregiving mothers' telomere length revealed that their cells had aged an additional nine to seventeen years faster than the low-stress group's regular aging rate. What explains how stress affects the body? Direct effects, such as long-term immune system suppression, stickier-than-normal platelets, slowed wound healing, constricted significant blood vessels, and indirect effects on behavior are some of the reasons stress may be harmful. People have a variety of unhealthy ways to react to stress. There are undoubtedly negative effects of risky behavior, such as overeating, smoking, drinking excessively, and not exercising enough. What is the meaning of this body of research to you? It implies that regular use of the techniques described in "How to prevent and manage stress" on page 10 will help you avoid or lessen the negative effects of stress. Strategies for reducing stress can be beneficial, but some conditions require additional care. The best course of treatment for you can be suggested by your doctor.

Cardiovascular disease refers to various conditions that impact the heart or the thousands of miles of blood vessels that carry oxygen and nutrients to every cell in the body. Atherosclerosis (the buildup of fatty deposits on artery walls), heart attacks, and strokes are three clear examples. According to the seminal Framingham Heart Study, certain factors increase cardiovascular disease risk. Some factors are out of your control, including race, age, sex, and genetics. However, you have some power over others. The "controllable" risk factors in the past have included smoking, inactivity, being overweight, having high blood pressure and cholesterol, and having diabetes. Stress on the mind seems to be a significant risk factor as well. Following the terrorist attacks of September 11, one three-year study asked 2,700 American adults to complete an online survey about their physical and mental health. Compared to those who experienced low levels of stress, those who experienced high levels right after the attacks were nearly twice as likely to develop high blood pressure and more than three times as likely to experience heart problems over the next two years. The development of cardiovascular disease is also thought to be significantly influenced by several psychological and social factors, such as caregiver stress, depression, anxiety, anger, and hostility, as well as a lack of social support, marital stress, work stress, and low socioeconomic status. Each of these factors increases the risk of heart disease when acting alone. Their combined strength grows exponentially. Positively, treating depression, managing hostility, and anger, and enhancing social support can all reduce your risk of developing cardiovascular disease. How might stress affect the risk of heart disease? Various options are being investigated. Adrenaline and other stress hormones released into the bloodstream seem to increase the body's production of cholesterol. The sympathetic nervous system can undergo changes that raise the risk of heart disease when it is aroused repeatedly. As an illustration, blood pressure increases, and platelets harden when the sympathetic nervous system is activated. While persistently high blood pressure harms the heart, blood vessels, and other organs and significantly raises your risk of developing heart disease, stickier platelets increase the likelihood of blood clots.

Inflammation and immune system dysregulation has also been linked. Heart attacks and clogged arteries caused by cholesterol are primarily caused by chronic inflammation. White blood cells of various types, the antibodies they produce, and a bewildering variety of chemical messengers known as cytokines all participate in the complex dance of inflammation. Its functions include clearing away debris, assisting in tissue repair, and protecting the body from bacteria, viruses, and other foreign invaders. But inside the arteries, inflammation both initiates and maintains atherosclerosis. Chest pain, a heart attack, or a stroke can be brought on by the dangerous blood vessel narrowing caused by atherosclerosis. Even artery-blocking clots, the primary cause of many strokes and heart attacks, are affected by inflammation.

Additionally, stress has an indirect effect because negative emotions cause people to act in ways that increase their risk of cardiovascular disease. Stressed-out individuals are more likely to smoke and less likely to exercise. Additionally, studies have shown that mental stress can cause sudden coronary artery spasms, at least when people with pre-existing heart disease must solve complex equations during laboratory experiments. A heart attack or temporary chest pain may result from a sudden spasm that blocks blood flow to a portion of the heart.

Can anxiety lead to cancer? There isn't any proof yet that stress can cause this. It is essential to look more closely at the possibility that long-term stress may affect immune defenses and thus contribute to disease. According to one theory about how cancer develops, cancerous cell changes frequently happen for several reasons, but the immune system identifies the cells as abnormal and eliminates them. Cancer cells can only increase once the immune system is compromised. Chronic stress can weaken the immune system, affecting how well the body can stop the unchecked growth of cancerous cells. But it is undeniable that stress management can aid in cancer recovery. A 2005 study of women receiving breast cancer treatment found that high-stress levels before diagnosis were associated with lower physical and emotional well-being following treatment and even a year later.

Your heart pumps blood throughout your body to maintain circulation. Millions of cells are supplied with nutrients and oxygen by this blood, and it also transports waste products from metabolism, such as carbon dioxide, to the organs that dispose of it. The blood pressure measures the force that propels the blood. Throughout the day, blood pressure varies, rising when you exercise or become agitated and falling when you relax or sleep. Your heart beats faster, and your blood pressure increases when stress hormones are released. Frequently, once a threat has passed, this rise is momentary, and your heart rate and blood pressure return to normal. Blood pressure, however, might continue to be consistently high if the stress response is repeatedly triggered. Hypertension, or high blood pressure, is risky for several reasons. It makes the heart work harder to pump blood through the body. The heart's muscles eventually thicken in response. However, this does not always equate to increased strength. In actuality, the blood supply to the heart frequently doesn't rise to the same extent, which causes the heart to weaken over time. Heart failure may result from this. In addition to damaging artery walls, high blood pressure also encourages atherosclerosis. Atherosclerosis can cause various health issues, including angina (chest pain), heart attacks, strokes, and kidney damage by constricting arteries and obstructing blood flow. The risk of a heart attack, heart failure, stroke, and kidney disease increases with blood pressure.

According to studies, the immune system is impacted by short-term stressors like exams or minor collisions and long-term stressors like a demanding job or a lingering argument with a spouse. Although a lot of research has been done on this subject, it is still unclear how stress affects the body's capacity to fight off disease until the science of human immunity is better understood. The immune system's activity does, however, temporarily increase in response to short-term stress. For instance, it has been demonstrated to increase the transfer of lymphocytes, which fight infection, from the bloodstream to the skin, which some researchers believe may help prevent disease and speed up healing. But persistent stress seems to affect some immune cells differently. Chronic stress, for instance, may suppress natural killer cells, which attack virus-infected cells and some tumor cells. Viruses may also take advantage of the stress-induced vulnerability. How quickly does the immune system recover from stress? That depends on the person and the stressor's initial cause. But after earthquakes and hurricanes, alarming changes in immune function persisted for weeks and months. Natural killer cells were found significantly suppressed among caregivers in one study of current and former spouses of patients with Alzheimer's disease compared to a control group. On average, this immune system suppression persisted for three years after the caregiver's duties were finished.

Inside the lungs, there are tiny airways called bronchioles. As oxygen passes through them, it enters the alveoli, which release it into the bloodstream. As you breathe, the lungs expel the carbon dioxide accumulated in the alveoli's blood and return through the bronchioles. The bronchioles are dilated and constricted by the autonomic nervous system. Bronchiolole constriction, which makes it harder to move air into and out of the lungs, can be brought on by strong arousal. As a result, stress and strong emotions like fear or anger frequently cause asthma attacks (bursts of breathlessness and wheezing) in some people with asthma. Of course, physical stressors like exercise and cold weather can have a similar effect. The extent to which stress contributes to the emergence of asthma is still up for debate. One of the main risk factors has been suggested to be early, severe family stress. However, other factors like genetic predisposition, exposure to specific allergens, viral infections, and elevated blood levels of particular allergy markers are also considered significant.

Gastrointestinal discomfort and other bowel symptoms can be brought on by a confluence of psychological and physical factors. Additionally, it was mentioned that for patients in gastrointestinal clinics, significant life stress frequently precedes the onset of functional bowel disorders. According to laboratory studies, the digestive system reacts to emotional arousal and mental stress. Heartburn and esophageal inflammation can result from an increase in gastric acid secretion. Ulcer growth may also be influenced by stress.

Additionally, stress can lead to abnormal colon and small intestine contractions, which can slow down the passage of food through the digestive system. Interestingly, the change in colonic contractions and the rise in gastric acid are caused by the parasympathetic nervous system, which returns the body to normal after the stress response occurs. What's more intriguing is that each person reacts to stress differently in their digestive system. One illustration of this variation is stress-related irritable bowel syndrome (IBS). Abdominal discomfort without a clear organic cause and abnormal contractions of the large and small intestines are characteristics of IBS. Two English gastroenterologists discovered that patients with IBS who typically experienced constipation moved food more slowly through the small intestine when under stress. For those who frequently experienced diarrhea, the opposite was accurate. IBS flare-ups can be triggered by a wide range of factors. A high-fat diet, specific hormones that impact the digestive system, and everyday stressors like conflict or work deadlines are a few. According to some research, IBS and peptic ulcer disease are more common than usual in people who lost one or both of their parents young due to death or divorce.

Chapter six

Your guide to stress relief

———

E ven the best book on stress management won't help you if you can't find the time to read it. If you only have a short time, consider using the stress-relieving tips discussed in this section. You can find ways to make your day easier whether you have a minute or a half hour. Sometimes it can be stressful to consider starting a program to manage stress. Start small and enjoy your successes rather than stopping in your tracks. Give yourself a week to concentrate on workable solutions that could assist you in managing just one stressor or obstacle in your life. Check to see if these solutions apply to one of your problems. Reduce the impact of ten everyday stressors:

1. Are you often late? Use time-management strategies. Take into account your priorities (and make time for yourself), then assign or eliminate unnecessary tasks. Make a segment-by-segment schedule for your day, allotting time for writing and phone calls. If you tend to overestimate your travel time, consistently allow yourself an additional 15 minutes or more to get where you're going. If being late results from procrastination, think about the underlying problem. Are you worried about what will occur once you arrive at work or a social event, for instance? You might also attempt to complete too many tasks in too little time.

2. Frequently angry? Think about the influence of cognitive distortions. Do you exaggerate a problem, make assumptions, or use emotional reasoning? Spend some time pausing to think, breathe, and make a decision.

3. *Are you unsure of your abilities?* Never attempt to go it alone. Speak to a cooperative coworker or your boss if the issue is work-related. Call the neighborhood library or a company that can provide the information you require, consult a knowledgeable friend, or asks around. Make a list of alternative approaches to obtaining the required knowledge or abilities. If you need a little tutoring, try using tapes, books, or classes, for instance. This is also effective when learning relaxation response techniques.

4. *Exhausted?* At least one time-consuming household task should be completed. Hire a housekeeping service, do your grocery shopping online, call a family meeting to decide who should do what chores, or pay or barter with teens to help around the house and yard. Think about what matters most and what might be put on hold.

5. *Not enough time to destress?* Try taking short breaks. Alternatively, promise yourself that you will reduce your to-do list for just one week so you can practice the relaxation response each day. One of the best ways to relieve stress is to slow down and focus on just one activity or pleasure at a time.

6. *Are you excruciatingly tense?* Take a mindful walk, get a massage, take a hot bath, do some mini-relaxations, or do a body scan. Any exercise, a brisk walk, a sprint up and down the stairs, or even a quick run, will be beneficial. Regular exercise and relaxation techniques both help to reduce stress.

7. *Do you tend to be pessimistic?* Remind yourself of the benefits of learned optimism, including a happier life and possibly better health. Develop your ability to dispel mental distortions. Read amusing books and rent comedic movies. Make a mental list of all the things for which you are thankful. If the list seems too condensed, consider expanding your social circle and adding more creative, beneficial, and leisure activities to your schedule.

8. Upset by disputes with other people? Avoid using zingers like "you always" or "you never" and instead express your needs or distress directly. "I feel _____when you _____," say you. "I would be so grateful if you could ." "I require assistance in prioritizing. What should I complete first, and what should I leave for later? Consider enrolling in an assertiveness training course if conflicts cause you a lot of stress.

9. Exhausted or worn out? Put an emphasis on self-nurturing methods. Make time to practice your relaxation response or, at the very least, indulge in short relaxation. Take good, healthy food into your body, and seek out other people to help you with your heart. Consider engaging in productive, leisurely, and creative activities. Think about your priorities in life: Is it worthwhile to feel this way, or is there another option available to you? If you want assistance, think about the best type. Do you want to have the job done for you? Do you want to complete it later? Do you require the assistance of someone with a specific skill set?

10. Do you feel lonely? Relate to others. Even small interactions, a quick exchange about local events with a neighbor, a question for a coworker, or a brief conversation in line at the grocery store, can help you break the ice. It might inspire you to look for more opportunities to connect as well. Donate your time. Attend religious or civic gatherings. Offer to go out for coffee with a friend. Contact a friend or family member you miss. Attend a captivating class. Seek assistance if social anxiety, low self-esteem, or depression prevent you from reaching out. When you share in the world's joys and sorrows, the world is a friendlier, more wonderful place.

While in the dentist's chair, mini-relaxations can help calm your anxiety and lessen your discomfort. They can reduce stress before a crucial meeting, in traffic, or when dealing with irritable people or circumstances. Here are some quick relaxation methods you can use.

When you have 1 minute

To feel your belly's gentle rise and fall as you breathe, place your hand just below your navel. Inhale slowly. Let's pause for three counts. Breathe out. Let's pause for three counts. Continue to inhale and exhale for one minute while waiting for a count of three between each breath. Alternately, while seated comfortably, take a few slow, deep breaths, repeating to yourself in a quiet voice, "I am" as you inhale and "at peace" as you exhale. Repeat two or three times slowly. Feel your entire body, then unwind into the chair's support.

When you have 2 minutes

Slowly count down from ten to zero. Take a full breath, inhaling and exhaling, for each number. Take a deep breath telling yourself "10," for instance. Exhale gradually. Say "nine" on your next breath, and so forth. Count down slowly and space your breaths farther apart if you feel dizzy. It would help if you experienced a sense of calmness once you reached zero. In that case, repeat the exercise.

When you have 3 minutes

Take a break from what you're doing and check your body for tension while sitting down. Relax the facial muscles, and let your jaw open a little. Drop your shoulders. Allow your arms to droop by your sides.

So that there are spaces between your fingers, let your hands relax. Do not cross your ankles or legs. Let your legs naturally fall apart as your thighs sink into the chair. Feel your calves and shins getting heavier as your feet sink deeper into the ground. Now take a deep breath in and another deep breath out.

When you have 5 minutes

Test out self-massage. To relieve muscle tension, use a variety of strokes. Use your hands edges as gentle chops, or tap with your fingers or palms cupped. Apply fingertip pressure to any knotted muscles. Knead across the muscles while attempting long, light strokes. Any body part within easy reach of you can receive these strokes. Try concentrating on your neck and head for a brief session like this.

- Begin by massaging the back of your neck and shoulder muscles. Make a loose fist and quickly rub the back and sides of your neck with it. Next, make little circles with your thumbs around the base of your skull. With your fingertips, gently massage the remaining portion of your scalp. Next, tap your scalp with your fingers as you move them over the sides, back, and front.
- Give your face a massage now. Use your thumbs or fingertips to create a string of tiny circles. Pay close attention to the muscles in your jaw, forehead, and temples. Start by massaging your nose bridge with your middle fingers, then move outward over your brows and to your temples.
- Lastly, shut your eyes. For a brief period, take a few easy breaths in and out while cupping your hands loosely over your face.

When you have 10 minutes

Try visualizing. Start by finding a quiet place to sit down. For a few minutes, take deep breaths. Imagine yourself now in a location that brings back pleasant memories. What do you smell—the potent fragrance of roses on a hot day, the crisp autumn air, or the hearty aroma of baking bread? Do you hear anything? Take in the shapes and colors that are all around you. Concentrate on enjoying your senses: the swooshing of a gentle breeze; the feel of cool, soft grass under your feet; the salty smell and rhythmic beat of the ocean. Intruding thoughts can be passively observed before being gently let go so you can return to the world you've created.

You may feel happier if you reflect on the good times, emotions, and relationships in your life. A gratitude journal is a helpful tool for recognizing your life's positive aspects and shifting your attention away from unfavorable feelings and thoughts. Keep a journal by your bed so that you can take five to ten minutes each evening to write about something for which you are thankful. Enjoy pleasant sights, sounds, and sensations like a sunset, birds chirping outside your window, your child is giving you a hug, or a friend's phone call. Celebrate big and small victories, such as mastering a new hobby, completing a task successfully at work, or getting the kids off to school on time. Imagine the scene in your mind and describe it in detail in your writing. Then take a moment to fully appreciate the experience once more. This journal can also be used to reflect on the things you are thankful for from the past.

Don't miss out!

Visit the website below and you can sign up to receive emails whenever Brian Gibson publishes a new book. There's no charge and no obligation.

https://books2read.com/r/B-A-EUPV-QHXDC

BOOKS 2 READ

Connecting independent readers to independent writers.

Also by Brian Gibson

Guide to Entrepreneurship Everything you Need to Know Before Becoming an Entrepreneur and Starting a Successful Business
Successful Introvert in Extroverted World Complete guide for introverts who want to make friends, be social, and build leadership abilities and developing powerful skills
The Skateboarding Culture From the Underground Movement Into the Mass Culture
Loving Your Pet The Ultimate Guide for Your Dog's Health, Food, Medical Care, Training, and Tricks
The Ultimate Guide to Manage and Stress Relief how to Identify Your Stress Warning Signs and Learn how to Better Manage Stressful Situations

Lightning Source UK Ltd.
Milton Keynes UK
UKHW020030110123
415109UK00015B/1044